THE GREAT BIG IRISH ANNUAL 2023

Gill Books

THIS BOOK BELONGS TO

NAME ....

ADDRESS ....

AGE ....

CONTENTS

Welcome to

THE GREAT BIG IRISH ANNUAL 2023!

INSIDE, YOU'LL FIND ...

LOTS OF FUN THINGS TO MAKE AND DO

CRAZY FACTS AND SILLY SCIENCE

HECTIC HISTORY AND SERIOUS SPORTS

... AND MUCH, MUCH MORE.

This is **YOUR BOOK**. You can **DOODLE** on it, **RIP IT UP**, **STICK PAGES ON YOUR WALL**, and **EVEN USE IT FOR LOO PAPER** (well, we'd prefer if you didn't do that).

so jump in!

YOUR BEST BiTS

The year 2022 was a **pretty crazy** time for everyone. How was your year?

MY **FAVOURITE** PART OF THE YEAR WAS ...

MY **LEAST FAVOURITE** PART OF THE YEAR WAS ...

THIS YEAR, **I LEARNED** ...

THIS YEAR, **I GREW** ...

THIS YEAR, **I TRIED** ...

THIS YEAR, **I VISITED** ...

IN 2023, **I WANT TO** ...

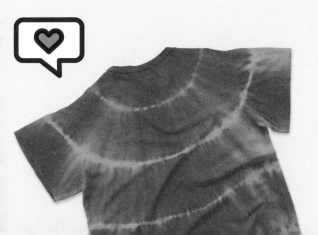

HISTORY BUFFS

The more you know about the past, the better prepared you are for the future!

2022 FLASH BACK

15 YEARS AGO ...

The very first iPhone was announced, and our texting thumbs have been sore ever since.

50 YEARS AGO ...

At the Munich Olympic Games, Mary Peters from Belfast became the first Irish woman to win a gold medal.

100 YEARS AGO ...

In Minnesota, Ralph Samuelson used a pair of boards and a clothesline to invent waterskiing.

25 YEARS AGO ...

The first book in the Harry Potter series was published, kicking off a global phenomenon. Wingardium Leviosa!

300 YEARS AGO ...

The famous pirate, Black Bart, is finally defeated in battle by the British Navy. H-arrr-d luck!

WHY WAS IT CALLED THE DARK AGES?

BECAUSE THERE WERE SO MANY KNIGHTS!

CRISS-CROSSING THROUGH HISTORY

ACROSS

5. Ireland is sometimes known as the _____ Isle.
6. Bram Stoker wrote _____ about this famous bloodsucker.
7. This unlucky ship was built in Belfast in 1912.
9. Before the Euro, this was Ireland's official currency.
10. The Romans called Ireland Hibernia, which means the land of _____.
11. The first name of the two female presidents of Ireland.
12. During the Iron Age, these settlements were built on an island in the middle of a lake.

DOWN

1. Queen Medb of Connacht fought a war to steal this animal.
2. The ancient Irish tradition of _____ inspired Halloween.
3. Grace O'Malley had this salty career.
4. An ancient Irish language that was carved onto rocks.
8. This ancient passage tomb is located in Co. Meath.

ARTY ALPHABET

Written in the 9th century, **THE BOOK OF KELLS** is filled with beautiful decorations.

The **FIRST LETTER** on each page was often decorated with strange, mythical animals.

Can you turn the first letter of **YOUR NAME** into a marvellous beast?

USE THESE FOR INSPIRATION.

3

JOKES AND RIDDLES

Try out these brainteasers on your friends and watch them scratch their heads!

WHAT GROWS IF YOU FEED IT, BUT DIES IF YOU WATER IT?

Fire

I'M TALL WHEN I'M YOUNG, AND I'M SHORT WHEN I'M OLD. WHAT AM I?

A candle

WHAT MONTH HAS 28 DAYS?

All of them

WHAT DOES A HOUSE WEAR?

Address

WHAT CAN YOU PUT IN A BUCKET OF WATER TO MAKE IT LIGHTER?

A hole

WHAT DO YOU CALL AN ARTISTIC LOBSTER?

Leonardo da Pinchy

WHY DID THE PHARAOH VISIT THE DENTIST?

Because Egypt his tooth.

WHAT HAS A BOTTOM AT THE TOP?

Your legs

RIDDLE ME THIS!

WHERE WAS THE IRISH PROCLAMATION SIGNED?

At the bottom

WHAT CAN BE CAUGHT BUT NOT THROWN?

A cold

WHAT'S HEAVIER — A KILO OF COTTON WOOL OR A KILO OF BRICKS?

They're the same weight.

A TOURIST WALKS INTO A ROMAN CAFÉ, HOLDS UP TWO FINGERS TO ORDER AND IS SURPRISED WHEN THEY GET FIVE COFFEES. WHY?

Because V is the Roman numeral for five.

WHAT WORD IS SPELLED WRONG IN THE DICTIONARY?

Wrong

WHAT'S ORANGE AND SOUNDS LIKE A PARROT?

A carrot

WHAT DID 0 SAY TO 8?

Nice belt

SCIENCE LAB

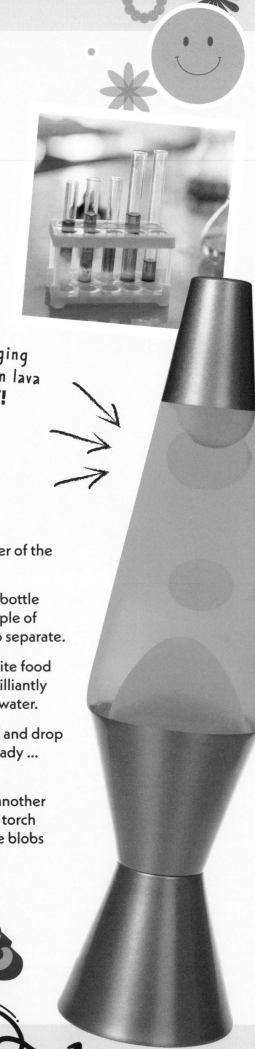

Feeling a bit **INVENTIVE**? Curious about how the world works? Or do you just feel like **MAKING A BIG MESS?**

Head back to the swinging '60s with your very own lava lamp. **GROOVY, BABY!**

LAVA LAMP

What you'll need

a clean plastic bottle

water

vegetable oil

food colouring

fizzing tablets

a torch

1. Fill the bottle up about a quarter of the way with water.

2. Pour the vegetable oil into the bottle until it is almost full. Wait a couple of minutes for the oil and water to separate.

3. Add a few drops of your favourite food colouring – blue or red work brilliantly – and let it spread out into the water.

4. Break your fizzing tablet in half and drop one part into the bottle. Get ready ... here comes the lava!

5. Turn off the lights and drop in another half tablet. This time, shine the torch through the lava lamp while the blobs are bubbling for a disco feel.

SMARTY PANTS!

The oil and water stay separated because oil is denser than water. The tablets release bubbles of gas, which float because they are lighter than the liquids.

TRUE OR FALSE?

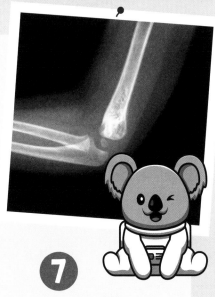

1 The chemical formula for water is H_2No.
✓ ✗

2 Sound travels four times faster in water than it does in air.
✓ ✗

3 Astrobiology is the study of life in space.
✓ ✗

4 Water boils at 1,000 degrees Celsius.
✓ ✗

5 Some animals have blue blood.
✓ ✗

6 The Earth is a perfect sphere.
✓ ✗

7 Australia is wider than the moon.
✓ ✗

8 The funny bone is another name for the humerus.
✓ ✗

9 Baking yeast is a type of fungus.
✓ ✗

10 Gravity only affects objects here on Earth.
✓ ✗

MAKE THE MATHS MATCH

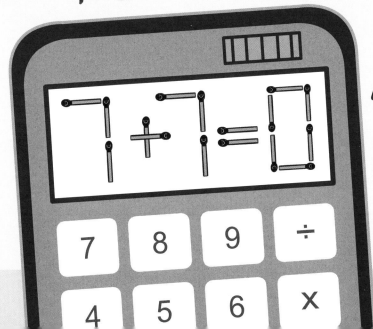

You light my fire.

Hmm ... something's not right here. Can you **MOVE** just **ONE** matchstick to make this sum correct?

Can you also solve this by **TAKING AWAY** one match?

| 7 | 8 | 9 | ÷ |
| 4 | 5 | 6 | × |

Whether you're as **WISE AS AN OWL**, as **SLIPPERY AS AN EEL**, as **SLY AS A FOX** or as **GIDDY AS A GOAT**, there's plenty of fun to be had in the **ANIMAL WORLD**.

WILD AT HEART

COLLECTIVE CHAOS

Everyone knows that a group of dogs is called a pack and a group of cows is a herd. But some other animals have very silly group names!

See if you can match them up.

A _____ OF PARROTS   POD

A _____ OF DOLPHINS   TOWER

A _____ OF CROWS   CRASH

A _____ OF OWLS   CACKLE

A _____ OF FOXES   RAFT

A _____ OF FROGS   ARMY

A _____ OF GIRAFFES   SKULK

A _____ OF HYENAS   MURDER

A _____ OF OTTERS   PARLIAMENT

A _____ OF RHINOCEROSES   PANDEMONIUM

CAN YOU COME UP WITH A FEW OF YOUR OWN?

A _____ OF _____

A _____ OF _____

A _____ OF _____

8

YES NO
PET SHOW

Here's a game you can play in the car, over dinner, in the dentist's waiting room ... or just about anywhere, really!

Pick an animal to be your pet. The more unusual the better – or maybe you could be sly and pick a really simple one.

Now, your friend has to guess what your pet is by asking questions. You can only answer yes or no.

Here are some good questions to start with:

Do you have a tail?

Do you have fur?

Are you dangerous?

Do you live in the ocean?

Are you bigger than a horse?

Do you have scales?

Do you eat plants?

Do you stand on four legs?

BEAST CHIC

Animals use all sorts of **patterns** to help them **blend into their surroundings**. But hiding all the time is boring – it's time to **stand out**! Can you come up with a **new pattern** for a fashion update?

SMARTY PANTS!

The grey wolf once roamed the Irish countryside, but sadly the last one was killed in 1786. Some people think that they should be brought back to the country through rewilding. Arrrooo!

9

ST BRIGID'S DAY

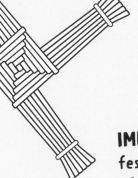

St Brigid's Day falls on 1 February, which is also the festival of Imbolc. In 2023, Ireland will celebrate this special day with a public holiday for the very first time.

IMBOLC was an ancient festival that marked the end of winter and the **BEGINNING OF SPRING** – a new season of life, hope and growth.

Spring also means the fields are full of leaping lambs – but can you spot the sleeping one?

FLOWER POWER

Can you match these spring flowers with their names? Try to collect one of each and glue them here!

SNOWDROP   TULIP   BLUEBELL

BUTTERCUP   DAISY   CROCUS

ST BRIGID'S CLOAK

St Brigid wanted to build a monastery in Kildare, but the King was super stingy. So she asked for just the amount of **land that her cloak could cover**.

The King looked at her small cloak, laughed and agreed. Then her cloak **began to spread out** in all directions – north, south, east and west – until it was **HUGE**.

The King was amazed and gave her all the land that her cloak covered. Can you **colour in this picture of St Brigid's cloak**?

SMARTY PANTS!

Brigid was also the name of a Celtic goddess who was born into an ancient tribe called the Tuatha Dé Danann. She was linked to fire, healing, crafts and poetry. Many historians believe that this goddess and St Brigid are the same mythological person.

GAGA FOR GAA

ARE YOU AN ALL STAR IN TRAINING?
A MASTER OF SOLOS OR AN EXPERT POINT
KICKER? A HURLING HERO OR A CÚL KID?

spot the difference

Can you **spot the difference**
between these two pictures?
There are **five** in total.

GIVE IT A HURL!

SMARTY PANTS!

The Poc Fada competition
comes from the Irish legend of
Cúchulainn, who set out from
his home to the King's court,
hitting his sliotar before him
and running ahead to catch it.

HiT iT FADAAAAAAA!

Every year, the Poc Fada championship takes place in Louth.

Top hurling and camogie players have to hit a sliotar along a 5km course through the mountains.

Can you help this player get to the end?

TRY FOR A TROPHY

Have you ever dreamed of holding the Sam Maguire or the Liam MacCarthy Cup? In the meantime, you can design your very own trophy here.

MAKE SURE TO ADD IN YOUR TEAM'S NAME!

CREATIVE CRAFTS

Lilly Higgins is a writer, TV chef and food photographer. She lives in Cork with her husband and three children.

Lilly loves nothing more than pottering around the house creating a cosy, comfortable nest for herself and her family.

She's here to share a great project and some of her favourite crafting tips.

TIE-DYE TRICKS

What you'll need:

white cotton fabric (like an old school T-shirt)

white vinegar

water

rubber bands

For the dye:

raw beetroot (pink)

turmeric (yellow)

elderberries (blue)

spinach (green)

red cabbage (purple)

1. First, prepare your fabric for dyeing. Mix 1 part vinegar to 4 parts water in a large pot. Simmer your fabric in this pot for one hour before using. Then run the fabric under cold water and wring it out.

2. Use rubber bands to twist sections of the fabric and tie them up. The folds and creases will stay white, and the rest of the fabric will be dyed.

3. While the fabric is simmering, make your dye. Mix 1 part ingredients for the dye (e.g. 1 cup of shredded red cabbage or 1 tbsp turmeric) with 2 parts water (e.g. 2 cups water). Bring the mix to a boil and simmer for 1 hour to get an intense colour.

4. Next, strain out the dyeing materials so that you're left with the coloured water.

5. Put the fabric into the coloured water and leave it to sit until you're happy with the colour, for an hour or even overnight.

6. Pull out the fabric and rinse it in cold water. Remove the rubber bands and hang to dry.

Can tie-dye please never go out of fashion?! It's so much fun. I love experimenting with natural dyes, from earthy onion skin to pink beetroot and bright yellow turmeric.

YOU CAN SKETCH OUT YOUR DESIGN HERE FIRST:

LILLY'S TOP TIPS

1.
You can dye all sorts of things, like cotton T-shirts, bandanas, drawstring bags, socks – even shoes!

2.
Stuff made with natural fibres is best. Look on the label for cotton, rayon, hemp or linen.

3.
For the best colour combos, use two primary colours (red, yellow or blue).

4.
Dyeing is a messy business! Be sure to wear old clothes or an apron.

5.
Don't forget to wear gloves, or the dye will stain your hands.

15

OUTDOORS: WHAT'S OUTSIDE THE WINDOW? IS YOUR HOUSE UP IN THE AIR? IS IT UNDERWATER? UNDERGROUND? ON A DIFFERENT PLANET?

In **50 years**, the **world** will **look very different**.

Scientific advances, new technology and the **changing climate** will mean **our lives will be transformed!**

BEDROOM

WHAT KIND OF BED WOULD YOU HAVE? WOULD IT HOVER? HANG UPSIDE DOWN? BE SHAPED LIKE A POD?

LIVING ROOM

HOW MANY SCREENS WOULD YOU HAVE? WHAT ABOUT YOUR PET? IS IT A CLONED T-REX? A ROBO-CROC?

THE FUTURE

In **2073**, what will your **perfect home look like**?

ROOF:
WHAT'S ON THE ROOF? SOLAR PANELS? A FOREST? A MINI-OCEAN?

WINDOWS:
HOW DO YOU LEAVE YOUR HOUSE? A SLIDING POLE? AN ESCALATOR? MAYBE A FLOATING PLATFORM!

BATHROOM

AN AUTO-SHOWER? A FIZZY DRINK TAP? MAYBE YOU HAVE A ROBOT TO PASS YOU THE LOO PAPER!

SIGNPOST:
MAKE SURE YOU NAME IT!

'S
HOME

KITCHEN

DO YOU HAVE A ROBOT HELPER? WHAT ARE YOU EATING? FOOD MADE FROM INSECTS? ARTIFICIAL BURGERS? *PEOPLE?!*

THE ROCK OF CASHEL

The Rock of Cashel is a group of **ancient buildings** set on top of a hill in **Tipperary**. According to legend, the devil took a bite out of a nearby mountain. He spat the rock out of his mouth and it became the Rock of Cashel.

The Rock was the home of the **Kings of Munster**. **Brian Boru** was crowned High King at Cashel in **AD 978** and made it his capital. Later, it was given to the Church, who added a chapel and high crosses.

An old story says that **King Aengus** was baptised at Cashel by **St Patrick**. During the baptism, he accidentally **stabbed the King's foot with his bishop's staff** but the King kept quiet, thinking it was all part of the ceremony!

FIGHTING TALK

High King Brian Boru fought against the Vikings at the Battle of Clontarf.

The battle lasted from sunrise to sunset, and Brian Boru's armies managed to force the Vikings out of Dublin.

The Vikings often gave their weapons descriptive names like 'hole-maker' or 'gnawer'.

CHOOSE A NAME FOR YOUR SWORD AND WRITE IT HERE:

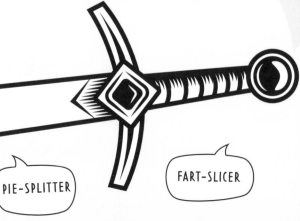

BUM-SCRATCHER

PIE-SPLITTER

FART-SLICER

CAPTURE THE CASTLE

From their **perch high up** on the Rock of Cashel, the High Kings could **see for miles**. This made it a perfect place to **defend against enemies**.

Can you **add some defences** to this castle before the army arrives?

A VIKING CALLED RUDOLF THE RED LOOKED OUT OF HIS WINDOW AND SAID, 'IT'S GOING TO RAIN.'

HIS WIFE SAID, 'BUT IT'S A NICE DAY — HOW DO YOU KNOW?'

'BECAUSE RUDOLF THE RED KNOWS RAIN, DEAR.'

HERE ARE SOME SUGGESTIONS:

LAVA MOAT

CANNONS

ANGRY BEES

BOOBY TRAPS

SPIKY DRAWBRIDGE

WATER GUNS

SLIPPERY LADDERS

TECH CORNER

Video games, science, robots and artificial intelligence – read all about it in the **Technology Times**!

The photographer is on their holidays. Can you fill in for them by drawing pictures to go with these news articles?

TECHNOLOGY TIMES

VINCENT VAN GOGHBOT

A company called OpenAI has created a digital artist called DALL·E 2. This artificial intelligence 'learns' from looking at huge numbers of pictures. You can put in some descriptive words, choose the style you like and DALL·E 2 will create a new work of art!

ROBO-CRAB

Engineers have created the smallest remote-controlled robot ever. Shaped like a crab, it's about as big as the width of a coin – even tinier than a flea! The tiny crab can walk, bend, twist, turn and jump. Luckily, it can't pinch just yet!

GIVE IT A POKE

In 2022 the Pokémon World Championship took place in Europe for the first time. Gamers from around the world traded cards and battled it out in tournaments to become the world champion. Gotta catch 'em all!

ELECTRIC CHOP

Scientists in Japan have developed chopsticks that are designed to help people cut down on salt. The chop-sticks use a tiny bit of electricity to make food seem saltier than it is. Imagine eating salt and vinegar crisps with chopsticks!

CRACK THE CODE

Want to write **SECRET MESSAGES** without your annoying brother reading them? Try this **DECODER RING** and you'll be **CODE-BREAKING IN NO TIME**.

WHAT YOU'LL NEED

Some card
Scissors
A split pin

1. Find a glass, bowl or something else circular. You'll need two, with one bigger than the other.

2. Place them on the card and draw around the bottoms to create two circles. Cut these out.

3. Once you have your circles, split them into 26 segments, like the templates on this page.

4. Write the alphabet around the outside of the bigger circle. Next, write the numbers 1 to 26 around the outside of the smaller circle.

5. Put the small circle on top of the bigger one and stick the split pin through the centre.

6. Turn the smaller wheel so that each number lines up with a different letter on the larger wheel.

7. Now you can create your secret message. For each letter, write down the number on the smaller wheel that appears directly beneath it.

IF **A = 1** AND **Z = 26**, CAN YOU CRACK THIS SECRET MESSAGE?

23-8-1-20   4-15
_____   _____

18-15-2-15-20-19   5-1-20
_____   _____

6-15-18   12-21-14-3-8-?
_____   _____

13-9-3-18-15   3-8-9-16-19-!
_____   _____

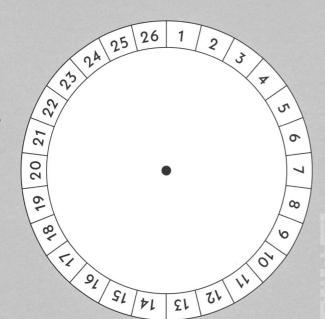

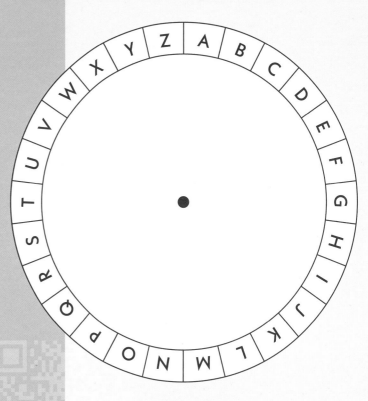

21

OUTER SPACE

Whether it's one small step or an epic lunar blast-off, you can rocket past the final frontier!

CAN YOU FIND ALL FIVE HIDDEN ALIENS?

WRITER'S ROOM

Lucy Kennedy is a writer and radio and television presenter. She lives in Dublin with her husband and three children.

CHATTING WITH LUCY KENNEDY

1. DID YOU ALWAYS WANT TO BE A WRITER?

Yes, I did. From the age of ten, I always said that I would one day write a children's book. I certainly wasn't expecting to write four! I do honestly believe that if you really, really want to write a book, then you will. It's that simple.

2. HOW DID YOU COME UP WITH THE IDEA FOR *THE FRIENDSHIP FAIRIES*?

I had an idea about three fairies who were sisters. I am one of three girls and having my own two little fairies at home, I am very much in the fairy zone! So I sat down and developed the idea over sheets and sheets of paper!

3. WHAT TIPS DO YOU HAVE FOR YOUNG WRITERS?

Give yourself the time to sit down with a pen and paper. You could be in the garden, at a desk, in bed, up a tree – it doesn't matter! Just make time to sit and think. The ideas will come along at the strangest of times, so always, ALWAYS carry a pen and a notebook with you.

4. TELL US A JOKE!

A horse walks into a classroom.

THE TEACHER ASKS: 'WHY THE LONG FACE?'

MAKING THE MAGIC HAPPEN

A CRANKY ELF
A BEE WITH A SORE BUM
A TALKING TEAPOT

First, you need a starring character:

Then you need a location for the story:

MOUNT EVEREST
UNDER YOUR BED
TÍR NA NÓG

Finally, you need a problem for them to face:

Lucy Kennedy's books were inspired by her family and her love of fairies. Use her tips to begin your own magical adventure!

A BROKEN WAND
AN EVIL DENTIST
TOXIC FARTS

NOW YOU'RE READY TO START YOUR STORY!

Introduce your character and setting

Now, give them a problem to solve

Then, give your story an ending ... to be continued?!

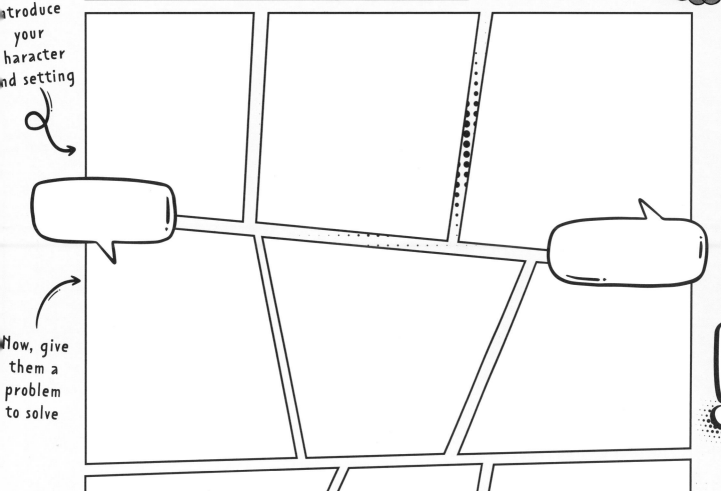

25

GREEN FOR GOOD

TRUE OR FALSE?

We all know that **our planet is in trouble**. Climate change is the **greatest threat facing the world** – and it's up to young people like you to fight back.

1 Biodiversity means the variety of life on Earth. ✓ ✗

6 A blue whale's heart is the size of a bumper car. ✓ ✗

7 Sir David Attenborough appeared in the 1993 movie *Jurassic Park*. ✓ ✗

2 You can find 10 million tiny blue-green algae in a teaspoon of seawater. ✓ ✗

5 Half of the world's species can be found in rainforests. ✓ ✗

8 Fruit flies were the first living creatures to be sent into space. ✓ ✗

4 Humans make up 50 per cent of life on Earth. ✓ ✗

9 Mosquitoes are attracted to smelly feet. ✓ ✗

10 There are no reptiles in Ireland. ✓ ✗

3 Birds, turtles and lobsters use smell to find their way. ✓ ✗

12 The largest living thing on Earth is a fungus. ✓ ✗

11 Hippopotamuses are closely related to dolphins and whales. ✓ ✗

BOMBS AWAY

Tip: Make sure your wildflower seeds are native to Ireland. Otherwise, they might hurt our local plants and animals.

Guerrilla gardeners (no, not gorillas!) like to spruce up boring urban spaces with **plants that look beautiful** and **help our local pollinators.**

Even if you live in an apartment or on a busy street, with these **seed bombs**, you can be a guerrilla gardener too!

WHAT YOU'LL NEED

500g compost
50g flour
Irish wildflower seeds

1. Mix together the compost, flour and seeds in a big bowl.

2. Slowly add water and mix into a sticky dough. Squish the mixture into palm-sized bombs.

3. Leave to dry for a day or two and they'll be ready to go.

4. Find a patch of grass near your home, a crack in a wall or even a pothole. It doesn't have to be a big space – every little bit helps.

5. Clear away any rubbish and big stones from your patch and loosen the soil.

6. Drop in your seed bomb and leave it to work its magic!

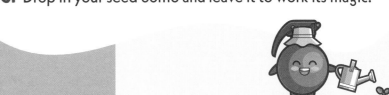

ACTION PLAN

It's natural to be worried about the future. But you can take that worry and **turn it into action** – action that will **make the planet a safer, healthier, greener place to live.**

☑ **MOVE GREEN**
Walk, cycle or use public transport

☑ **EAT GREEN**
Eat less meat and dairy

☑ **LIVE GREEN**
Only buy what you need

You could also **write a letter** to your local politician **using this template.** Make sure to cut it out and post it!

My name is _____ and I live in _____.

I want to know what you are doing about the CLIMATE EMERGENCY. I am particularly worried about _____ and _____.

I already do these three things to help:

_____

_____

_____

PLANET EARTH is in serious trouble. Our entire FUTURE is at stake and we are RUNNING OUT OF TIME.

If you LEADERS act like CHILDREN, us CHILDREN will have to act like LEADERS!

In fact, we'll do that anyway!

Yours sincerely,

_____

SPORTY SUPERSTARS

Ireland is bursting at the seams with talented sport stars. **KATIE TAYLOR, KELLIE HARRINGTON, LEONA MAGUIRE, RHYS McCLENAGHAN** and **ISRAEL OLATUNDE** have all been smashing it on the world stage! **COULD YOU BE NEXT?**

SPOT THE DIFFERENCE

Katie Taylor is looking fighting fit! Can you **spot the five differences** between these two photos?

PUTTER THERE

It's a windy day on the golf course, but there's still a chance of a hole in one.

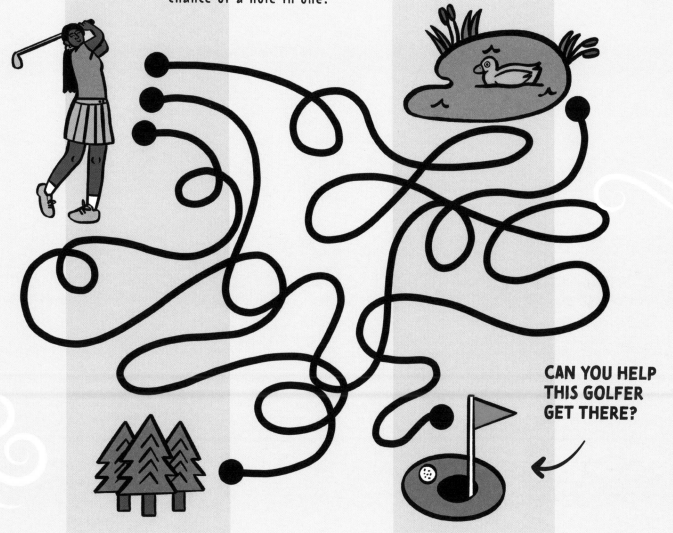

CAN YOU HELP THIS GOLFER GET THERE?

What do fishermen and boxers have in common?

They both throw hooks!

SMARTY PANTS!

Hundreds of years ago, Ireland had its very own Olympics. The Tailteann Games lasted 30 days and included athletics, swimming, sword fighting, boxing, archery and wrestling, along with funerals and arranged marriages!

KiTCHEN CORNER

TAKING THE CAKE

Can you **cut this cake** into **EIGHT** pieces using just **THREE** slices?

Hint: Try looking at the problem sideways ...

ARE YOU A MASTER CHEF OR CAN YOU BURN A GLASS OF WATER? BON APPÉTIT ...

DELICIOUSLY TRUE OR TASTELESSLY FALSE?

1. Green olives are just unripened black olives. _____

2. Dog food gets tested by humans. _____

3. Pizza got its name because each person gets a 'piece-a' it. _____

4. Ketchup pills were once used to treat illnesses. _____

5. Potatoes were the first vegetable to be grown in space. _____

6. Bananas are technically herbs. _____

7. Buffalo wings are made from the wings of a buffalo. _____

8. Peanuts grow underground. _____

9. A churro is made of donkey meat. _____

10. Paneer is a type of cheese used in Indian food. _____

YUM!

There's nothing like a 99 ice-cream on a sunny day. If you ask your parents, they'll say it's named after the original price – 99p. Wrong! It's actually named after the type of flake that is used. But why this particular bit of chocolate is called a 99 is lost in the mists of time …

UPSIDE-DOWNY- FROWNY-BROWNIE

This simple recipe for your own personal brownie will turn your frown upside down in just 5 minutes. It's dessert in a mug!

Tip:
Pick a nice big mug for your brownie and make sure it is microwave safe!

2 tablespoons melted butter

4 tablespoons plain flour

2 tablespoons sugar

2 tablespoons cocoa powder

3 tablespoons milk

2 drops vanilla extract

1. Put the flour, sugar and cocoa into your mug. Stir it up with a fork until the mixture looks like brown sand.

2. Stir in the butter until it makes a paste.

3. Then add the milk and vanilla extract and stir until smooth.

4. Microwave your mix on high power for 1 minute. After cooking, the brownie should still look a little bit wet – the mixture is very hot and is still cooking on the inside.

5. Let the brownie rest for four minutes. This is the hard part, but the wait is worth it! Then you can dig in with your favourite spoon.

CRAIC AGUS CEOL

IRELAND IS FAMOUS AROUND THE WORLD FOR OUR DANCING, OUR MUSIC AND OUR SENSE OF FUN

FLEADH-ED OUT

In **2022** the **Fleadh Cheoil** took place for the **first time in two years**. Traditional musicians of all ages gathered in the host town of **Mullingar** to sing and dance.

Can you **design a poster** for your town to host next year's Fleadh?

WELCOME TO _____ !

OUR MOST FAMOUS MUSICIAN IS

THE BEST PLACE TO DANCE IS

TRY THE FOOD AT

AND DON'T FORGET TO VISIT

FLEADH CHEOIL 2023

SMARTY PANTS!

Bodhráns were traditionally made with goatskin and were hit with a double-ended knuckle bone. Nowadays, synthetic materials are used – which must be a relief for the goats!

GLAD RA8S

CAN YOU **COLOUR IN** THIS DANCER'S DRESS WITH **BRIGHT COLOURS**?

HIT THE RIGHT NOTES BY FINDING THESE MUSICAL WORDS!

Q	N	I	Q	E	X	G	P	P	L	X	L	B	M	I
P	P	H	O	F	I	C	X	C	J	H	T	L	X	L
G	F	I	D	D	L	E	B	E	Q	Y	Q	E	Z	B
A	L	W	X	P	T	M	O	I	I	F	O	D	D	L
C	D	B	N	O	Z	V	D	L	V	I	M	R	H	U
C	N	O	O	L	C	I	H	I	Z	M	T	A	N	C
O	K	A	O	K	H	E	R	C	C	N	L	V	Z	Q
R	N	N	H	A	V	W	A	U	S	F	L	U	T	E
D	Z	V	D	O	T	I	N	W	H	I	S	T	L	E
I	M	L	Z	G	R	P	E	R	P	A	E	J	T	R
O	A	K	H	Z	Y	N	S	A	F	P	A	M	U	Q
N	Y	R	F	P	H	H	P	R	K	F	N	Z	E	B
Y	Z	D	Q	Y	K	L	V	I	X	M	N	X	G	W
K	E	X	P	F	A	O	E	Y	P	W	O	O	E	X
T	S	R	A	E	E	H	N	O	N	E	S	G	B	L

FIDDLE

ACCORDION

BODHRÁN

FLUTE

CÉILÍ

SEAN NÓS

HORNPIPE

POLKA

TIN WHISTLE

INTO THE WOODS

There's nothing better than an **ADVENTURE IN THE FOREST** ... as long as you've brought a **GOOD PICNIC!**

SUPER SHELTER

If you're **out in the wilderness**, the most important thing to know is how to **make a shelter**.

You can **practise this hut** at any stage, just for fun!

1. First, figure out which way the wind is blowing. Your shelter's door should face away from the wind.

2. Collect and gather your materials. You'll need some rope, two thick branches for your entrance and a long, strong branch to act as your 'pole'. You'll also need smaller sticks and leaves.

3. Push the thick branches into the ground to make your entrance. Cross them into an X shape and tie them tightly together.

4. Then, rest the long pole in the crook made by the X shape. Make sure you can fit underneath!

5. Lay smaller branches at an angle against the pole on both sides.

6. Then cover the structure with smaller branches and leaves. The thicker the walls, the better!

7. Chill out in your shelter. Maybe even have a nap!

TREE-MENDOUS

Trees produce fruit in order to pass on their seeds and hopefully grow new trees. Can you **match these fruits to their trees**?

CONKER	SYCAMORE
PINECONE	OAK
ACORN	IVY
HELICOPTER	PINE TREE
BERRIES	HORSE CHESTNUT

SMARTY PANTS!

Experts say that there are more than 60 different ways to use a bandana in a survival situation. How many ways can you think of?!

_____

_____

_____

TRACK LIKE A TROOPER

If you're out and about, it's important to leave tracks for your friends or family in case you split up or get lost.

Here are some trail signs you can leave in your path to make sure they know which way you've gone.

STRAIGHT AHEAD

TURN RIGHT

TURN LEFT

WRONG WAY

WATER AHEAD

OBSTACLE AHEAD

GONE HOME!

IRISH ADVENTURERS

From **AUSTRALIA** to **ZIMBABWE** and everywhere in between, these **IRISH EXPLORERS** found **ADVENTURES ALL OVER THE GLOBE!**

A WILD SiGHT

TOM CREAN was a polar explorer who spent many years in Antarctica. After his heroic adventures, he retired and ran a pub in Co. Kerry called the South Pole Inn.

Explorers always carry notebooks in case they **discover a new 'specimen'**. What have **you found** on your adventures?

DEAR DIARY,

I found a new specimen in the wild today!

It has _____ fur, a huge _____ and three pairs of _____.

It sounded like a _____ mixed with a _____.

I tried to take a picture, but it _____ the camera and _____, before running away!

I've drawn a picture here instead.

I'm going to call it the _____!

PACK IT IN

You're off on **two adventures** – first to the frozen **Arctic** waste and then to the sweltering **Amazon** jungle.

What should you **put in your two rucksacks**? Think about the **weather, animals, food, survival supplies** ...

ARCTIC VOYAGE

1 _____
2 _____
3 _____
4 _____
5 _____

POLAR BEAR DISGUISE

LOO PAPER WOOLLY SOCKS

MOSQUITO SPRAY CHOCOLATE BARS

AMAZON QUEST

1 _____
2 _____
3 _____
4 _____
5 _____

CYNTHIA LONGFIELD was an entomologist – a scientist who studies insects – and she travelled through the Amazon to collect moths, butterflies, dragonflies and beetles. Her nickname was Madame Dragonfly!

LIZZIE LEBLOND was a Victorian mountaineer and photographer. She climbed all over the Alps and Arctic Norway. At the time, women didn't usually go on adventures, so Lizzie often climbed in a heavy skirt!

ERNEST SHACKLETON was an explorer who travelled to Antarctica. On one adventure, his ship, the *Endurance*, became trapped in ice, and the crew had to abandon it. In 2022 the *Endurance* was finally found – 3,000 metres under the ice!

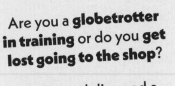

Are you a **globetrotter in training** or do you **get lost going to the shop**?

You'll need dice and a token for each player!

AROUND

START

END!

CHAT TO THE EASTER ISLAND STATUES
Miss a turn

SURF DOWN VICTORIA FALLS
Forward 1 space

FIGHT AT THE COLOSSEUM
Forward 2 spaces

FREEZE ON MOUNT EVEREST
Miss a turn

MEDITATE AT ANGKOR WAT
Forward 4 spaces

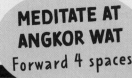

POLISH THE TAJ MAHAL
Miss a turn

THE WORLD

STRAIGHTEN THE LEANING TOWER OF PISA
Miss a turn

SLIDE DOWN THE GREAT PYRAMID OF GIZA
Back 2 spaces

NIP OVER THE GREAT WALL OF CHINA
Forward 1 space

CLIMB THE STAIRS TO MACHU PICCHU
Forward 1 space

FALL INTO THE GRAND CANYON
Back 3 spaces

THE ATLANTIC OCEAN

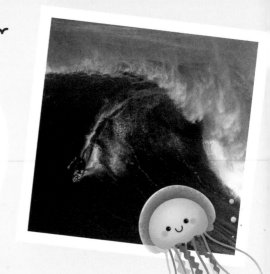

The ocean around us is teeming with life. It gives us our mild climate, beautiful beaches and delicious seafood. So dive in!

BITTA BEACHCOMBING

There are many **weird** and **wonderful things** to be found along the **Irish coast**.

Tick the box if you've seen any of these treasures – and if you haven't yet, **keep an eye out next time** you visit the beach!

SEA POTATO
The shell of a furry urchin

SEA GLASS
Smooth pieces of coloured glass weathered by the ocean

MERMAID'S PURSE
The egg case of a shark

GOOSE BARNACLES
Strange-looking barnacles from the deep sea

HAG STONES
Magical stones that have a natural hole in them

CUTTLEBONE
The inner shell of a cuttlefish

SMARTY PANTS!

Every year, about 8 million tons of plastic escape into the oceans from coastal countries like Ireland. That's like putting 5 bin bags full of rubbish on every foot of coastline around the world ... so please pick some up!

Tip: Make sure to leave everything as you found it – replace any rocks you turn over, put back any crabs or fish and don't scrape anything off its rocky home.

42

SEASHELL WINDCHIME

WHAT YOU'LL NEED

Some string
About 20 shells
A nice stick about as long as your forearm

Tip:
If you put a bit of baby oil on your shells once they're dry, they'll stay nice and shiny.

1. Wash your seashells with warm water and soap. If you skip this step, your windchime will be stinky!

2. When they're dry, ask a handy adult to carefully drill a small hole in each shell.

3. Cut four pieces of string of different lengths. Space them out along your stick and tie them with a nice tight knot.

4. Now, thread your shells onto each string, tying a knot to keep each one in place. Continue until you run out of shells.

5. Hang your windchime somewhere breezy and listen to the sound of the sea!

SURF'S UP!

The sun is out, the waves are high ... perfect day for a surf, dude! But this board is looking a little plain. **Can you juice it up with some rad decorations?**

Here are some gnarly ideas to inspire you.

43

HAUNTING HALLOWEEN

DID YOU KNOW THAT THE CELTS INVENTED HALLOWEEN?

During the ancient festival of Samhain, the Celts would light fires and wear costumes to scare away ghosts.

The people believed that this marked the end of summer and the beginning of the long, cold winter.

DISGUSTING DISHES

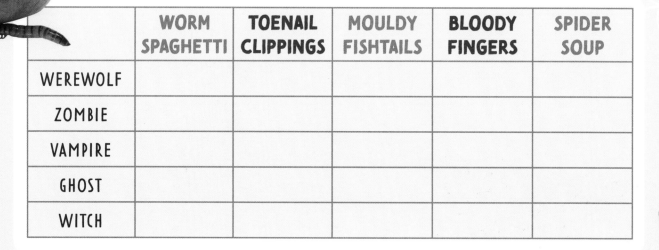

You're at a **Halloween party** and there's a **huge spread of revolting food**. But **some** of the **guests are picky eaters**.

Each guest had **one meal**. Can you figure out **who ate what**?

	WORM SPAGHETTI	TOENAIL CLIPPINGS	MOULDY FISHTAILS	BLOODY FINGERS	SPIDER SOUP
WEREWOLF					
ZOMBIE					
VAMPIRE					
GHOST					
WITCH					

CLUES:

The **werewolf** loves crunchy food.

The **vampire** is afraid of spiders.

The **ghost** loves seafood.

The **vampire** likes long, stringy food.

The **zombie** is allergic to pasta.

The **witch** likes to slurp her dish with a spoon.

BLOODY WITCHY FINGERS

These biscuit fingers are **BLOODY GOOD FUN**. Thankfully, they taste much better than they look!

WHAT YOU'LL NEED

175g plain flour
120g butter
50g sugar
Almonds
Raspberry jam

1. Preheat the oven to 160°C and line a tray with baking paper.

2. Mix the flour, sugar and butter in a food processor until it all comes together in a ball.

3. Flatten the dough, wrap it in plastic and put it in the fridge for one hour.

4. Roll out the dough into finger shapes. Use a cocktail stick to add wrinkly lines at the knuckles.

5. Put the fingers on the baking tray and bake for 12–15 minutes. Take them out and let them cool completely.

6. To decorate, put a blob of raspberry jam on the end of each finger and stick an almond on as a fingernail.

7. Dip the other ends of the fingers into the jam for a gruesome finish!

OMG!

What was your **HALLOWEEN OUTFIT THIS YEAR?**

_____

What do you want to go as **NEXT YEAR?**

_____

ARGH!

SMARTY PANTS!

In Germany, families hide all the knives in their homes around Halloween so that the returning spirits won't be hurt by them. They must believe in knife after death!

45

SOCCER SHOWDOWN

Are you a **SUPER STRIKER**, a **TOUGH DEFENDER**, a **GRACEFUL GOALIE** ... or just a regular **HEAD-THE-BALL**?

BEAT THE GOALIE

It's the final of the **2022 World Cup in Qatar**, and it's come down to a **penalty shootout**.

WHY DID THE CHICKEN GET A RED CARD?

FOR FOWL PLAY!

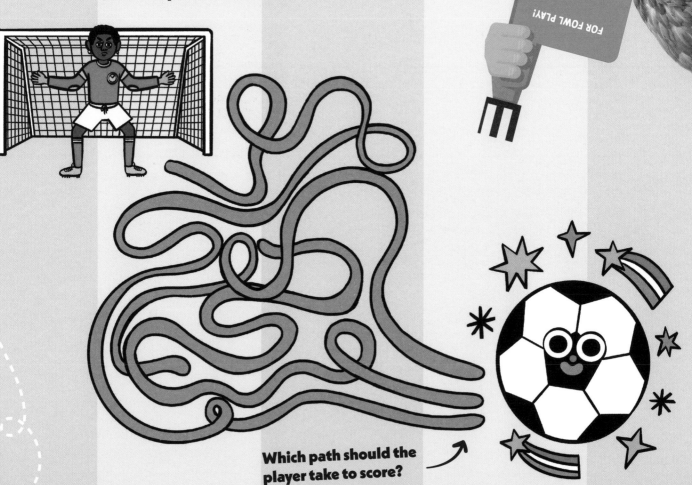

Which path should the player take to score?

DOTTY DRiBBLE

Can you follow the alphabet to finish off the soccer ball?

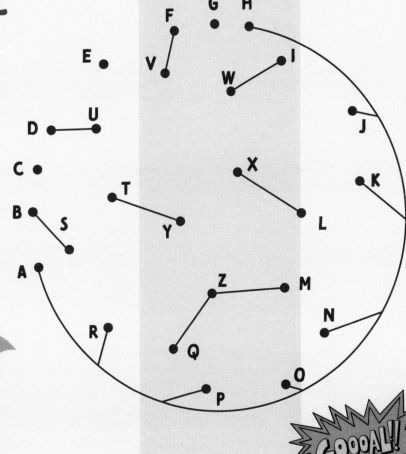

WHY WAS THE SOCCER FIELD WET?

THE PLAYERS DRIBBLED ALL OVER IT.

GOOOAL!!

RACK UP THE GOALS BY FINDING EACH OF THESE HIDDEN WORDS!

S	D	P	E	G	H	Y	A	D	I	B	R	F	T	P
O	K	O	Y	I	E	J	E	R	S	E	Y	T	G	Z
Y	Y	I	B	A	A	X	F	T	O	G	H	A	H	C
L	F	Y	N	U	D	F	C	S	S	M	S	C	X	I
C	P	N	G	B	E	R	W	H	G	M	H	K	F	O
O	U	C	O	B	R	C	I	H	O	W	E	L	O	X
R	C	D	A	S	P	I	G	B	I	M	M	E	U	P
N	Y	B	L	K	T	Z	O	G	B	S	C	T	L	P
E	W	O	I	Y	R	A	E	P	G	L	T	H	E	J
R	X	K	E	H	B	E	D	U	P	Z	E	L	G	P
D	N	A	W	O	K	G	M	I	Z	K	C	W	E	I
T	V	G	U	I	Q	Q	C	G	U	N	X	C	S	Y
T	V	G	E	I	B	P	U	E	K	M	E	Z	R	D
Q	U	K	R	E	F	E	R	I	E	E	C	M	Z	N	D
O	T	C	Z	W	V	I	X	Z	Y	I	V	X	V	U

WHISTLE

REFEREE

STADIUM

HEADER

TACKLE

DRIBBLE

JERSEY

CORNER

FOUL

GOALIE

47

AN EPIC ADVENTURE

There's nothing better than a story with lots of **magic**, **danger** and a **heroic quest**.

But first you'll need some characters: a **Champion** and a **Dark Lord** to fight the ultimate battle of **good versus evil**!

A CHAMPION IS BORN

CHOOSE YOUR CHAMPION:

_____

_____

APPRENTICE MAGE

KNIGHT'S SQUIRE

EXPERT THIEF

WOOD ELF

CENTAUR

CHOOSE YOUR WEAPON:

_____

_____

FIRE-THROWING

SILVER DAGGER

ENCHANTED SWORD

BOW AND ARROW

CHOOSE YOUR SIDEKICK:

_____

_____

_____

WHITE WOLF

PIXIE

SALAMANDER

NOW, DRAW YOUR CHAMPION HERE:

FINALLY, NAME YOUR CHAMPION:

_____

_____

GAVIN THE DRAGON-BOTHERER

DAISY THE PHANTOM FARTER

FINN FAST-FINGERS

THE SILVER ARCHER

THE DARK LORD RISES

BAM!

CHOOSE YOUR DARK LORD:

_____

_____

DEMON

WRAITH

SORCERER

BLOOD-SUCKER

CHOOSE YOUR MINIONS:

_____

_____

DARKHOUNDS

SKELETON BEARS

BAT-CATS

ARMY OF TROLLS

CHOOSE WHERE YOUR LAIR IS:

_____

_____

_____

IN AN UNDERGROUND MOUNTAIN CAVE

IN THE DEEP, DARK WOODS

IN A HUGE CITY FORTRESS

NOW, DRAW YOUR DARK LORD HERE:

FINALLY, NAME YOUR DARK LORD:

_____

_____

THE SHADOW KNIGHT

REALLY MEAN DAVE

QUEEN OF DARKNESS

MAXIMUS SKULL-MANGLER

DUBLIN AIRPORT

Dublin Airport **OPENED IN 1940** with just one flight a day, to Liverpool. In the 1950s, people used to **TRAVEL OUT TO THE AIRPORT JUST TO EAT** in its fancy restaurant.

DANCES WERE EVEN HELD in the terminal at night! A **NEW TERMINAL** opened in **1972**, and in 2010 **TERMINAL 2** was unveiled.

More than **400 MILLION PASSENGERS** have travelled through Dublin Airport since that first flight took off in 1940!

A WOMAN JUMPS FROM A PLANE WITHOUT A PARACHUTE BUT SHE LANDS WITHOUT ANY INJURIES. HOW CAN THIS BE?

THE PLANE WAS ON THE GROUND.

Lost Luggage

You've arrived at your holiday destination safe and sound! But ... your luggage hasn't.

Can you pick it out of this line-up?

1

2

3

4

LANDING GEAR

ENGINE

COCKPIT

CABIN

WING

RUDDER

HIGH FLIER

Can you match these labels to the right part of the plane?

TOY SHOW TIME

It's that time of year – time to stick on your pyjamas, stay up way past your bedtime and watch the *Late Late Toy Show*!

Every year, **RYAN TUBRIDY** wears lots of different Christmas jumpers as he hosts the Toy Show. Can you colour in this one for him? **MAKE IT AS COLOURFUL AND AS CHRISTMASSY** as you can!

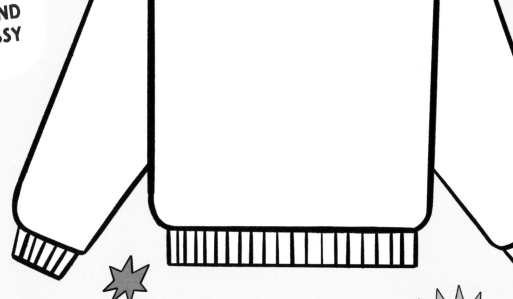

WHAT'S ON YOUR TOY SHOW WISH LIST?

SMARTY PANTS!

Every year, the *Late Late Toy Show* audience donates money to good causes across Ireland. In 2021 they raised over €5 million for charity!

MAJOR MALFUNCTION

The **Late Late Toy Show** is broadcast live, and we all know **things can go wrong** on the night! **Showers of slime, glitter bombs, exploding teddies** – it's all part of the show.

Imagine you're on stage, doing a demonstration of your favourite toy, and fill in the gaps.

'Next on stage is _____ who is from County _____.

They are showing off their favourite toy: _____.

This toy is great because it is _____ and _____.

Oh no! It's stopped working! Now Ryan Tubridy is covered with _____ and has _____ in his eye!

He'll have to change his jumper after this ...'

CHIP 'N' DIP

What did the hungry man say to the tortilla thief? That's nacho cheese! But you can make your own with this easy recipe.

For the chips:

6 corn tortilla wraps
olive oil
salt

For the salsa:

1 tin of chopped tomatoes
1 red onion
Half a lime, squeezed
1 garlic clove
1/2 red chilli
grated cheese

1. Preheat your oven to 200°C/180°C fan/gas 6.
2. Brush both sides of the wraps with oil, then cut them into triangles with scissors.
3. Line a tray with baking paper. Lay out the triangles in a single layer on the tray and bake for 7–8 minutes, turning them halfway.
4. Remove your chips, sprinkle them with salt and let them cool.
5. For the salsa, throw everything into a blender and blitz. You can have it chunky or smooth – it's up to you.
6. Put the chips in a wide dish and spoon the salsa over them. Sprinkle cheese on top and pop it in the oven until the cheese is melted. Careful – your dish might be hot.
7. Dip your chips and enjoy!

CHRISTMAS

IT'S FINALLY HERE!

Amazing Maths

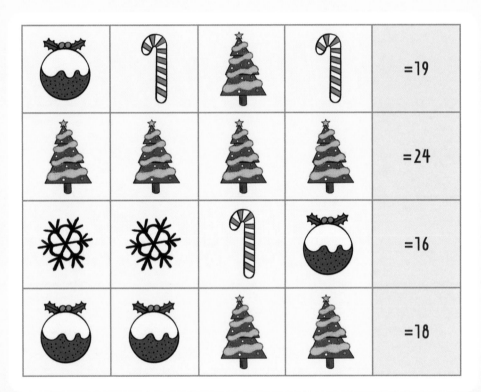

🍮	🍬	🎄	🍬	=19
🎄	🎄	🎄	🎄	=24
❄	❄	🍬	🍮	=16
🍮	🍮	🎄	🎄	=18

CAN YOU WORK OUT THE VALUE OF EACH ITEM?

SPELL IT OUT

How many four-letter words can you make out of the letters in

CHRISTMAS?

HERE'S A FEW TO START YOU OFF:

MISS

CHAT

SASH

54

WINTER WONDERLANDS

It's **not just Christmas** – many cultures **celebrate** festivals during the **winter**. Here are just a few:

The **WINTER SOLSTICE** takes place on the shortest day and longest night of the year.

DIWALI, the festival of lights, is a Hindu holiday that marks the beginning of a new year.

HANUKKAH is a celebration of religion and history for Jewish people.

BODHI DAY, the day of enlightenment, is a day of remembrance and meditation for Buddhists.

The **CHINESE NEW YEAR** follows the lunar calendar. 2023 will be the Year of the Rabbit!

MI   CKSI   FO   LIMK

___   ____   __   ____

NAD   KOOSCIE   DAN

___   _____   ___

OOST   KASEM   EM   ZEESEN!

____   _____   __   _____

KRIS KRINGLE is feeling a bit **KRIS CRANKY!** He's fed up with something ... can you **UNSCRAMBLE HIS MESSAGE** to find out why?

BiG QUiZ

How's your general knowledge? Were you paying attention this year? It's time to get quizzical ...

ROUND 1

1. What is the name of NASA's new space telescope?
2. What team won the 2022 All-Ireland Hurling Final?
3. Where in your body would you find your Achilles tendon?
4. What colour do tennis players wear at Wimbledon?
5. What band was Harry Styles in?
6. What type of animal is calamari?
7. What are the five colours of the Olympic rings?
8. What actor plays Doctor Strange in the Marvel universe?
9. Who lives next door to The Simpsons family?
10. What team won the UEFA Women's Euro 2022 Final?

ROUND 2

1. What is the main ingredient of guacamole?
2. How many notes are in a musical scale?
3. What is a baby hare called?
4. What team won the 2022 All-Ireland Football Final?
5. What colour is a giraffe's tongue?
6. Where is the smallest bone in the human body?
7. In the Harry Potter books, what does the Wingardium Leviosa spell do?
8. What country won the Eurovision in 2022?
9. What is the capital of Iceland?
10. Where would you find the original Legoland?

OF 2022!

ROUND 3

1. What do cryptozoologists study?

2. What colours are in the Italian flag?

3. What animal is on Bus Eireann's logo?

4. What food does a panda eat?

5. What town hosted the Fleadh Cheoil in 2022?

6. What is the smallest county in Ireland?

7. What are Shane Filan, Mark Feehily, Kian Egan and Nicky Byrne known for?

8. What is the most common surname in Ireland?

9. What are Granny Smiths and Pink Ladies?

10. What 2022 Disney movie stars a character first seen in Toy Story?

ROUND 4

1. What country hosted the 2022 FIFA World Cup?

2. What does WWW stand for in website addresses?

3. Who wrote The Hobbit?

4. What five counties border Northern Ireland?

5. What Irish journalist organised fundraising climbs all over the country in April?

6. What sport is Simone Biles famous for?

7. What poet is buried under Benbulben mountain?

8. What is the Irish word for apple?

9. What singer released an album called Renaissance in 2022?

10. What does RTÉ stand for?

ANSWERS

PAGE 3

ACROSS
5. Emerald
6. Dracula
7. Titanic
9. Punt
10. Winter
11. Mary
12. Crannóg

DOWN
1. Bull
2. Samhain
3. Pirate
4. Ogham
8. Newgrange

PAGE 7
1. **FALSE** – it's H_2O
2. **TRUE**
3. **TRUE**
4. **FALSE** – 100 degrees Celsius
5. **TRUE**
6. **FALSE** – it's squashed
7. **TRUE**
8. **TRUE**
9. **TRUE**
10. **FALSE** – it affects the whole universe

MAKE THE MATCHES MATCH

Take one match from one 7 and use it to make the 0 an 8 (1 + 7 = 8)

Remove one match from the plus sign to make a minus (7 – 7 = 0)

PAGE 8

A pandemonium of parrots
A pod of dolphins
A murder of crows
A parliament of owls
A skulk of foxes
An army of frogs
A tower of giraffes
A cackle of hyenas
A raft of otters
A crash of rhinoceroses

PAGE 12

PAGE 21

What do robots eat for lunch?

MICRO CHIPS!

PAGE 28
1. **TRUE**
2. **TRUE**
3. **FALSE** – they use magnetism
4. **FALSE** – just 0.01%!
5. **TRUE**
6. **TRUE**
7. **FALSE** – but his brother did!
8. **TRUE**
9. **TRUE**
10. **FALSE** – the common lizard
11. **TRUE**
12. **TRUE**

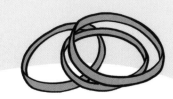

PAGE 30

PAGE 32

1. TRUE
2. TRUE
3. FALSE
4. TRUE
5. TRUE
6. TRUE
7. FALSE
8. TRUE
9. FALSE
10. TRUE

TAKING THE CAKE

Cut the cake in half, then into quarters. Then slice it horizontally to make eight pieces.

PAGE 37

conker = horse chestnut
pinecone = pine tree
acorn = oak
helicopter = sycamore
berries = ivy

PAGE 44

werewolf = toenail clippings,
zombie = bloody fingers,
vampire = worm spaghetti,
ghost = mouldy fishtails,
witch = spider soup

PAGE 54

tree = 6, pudding = 3,
candy cane = 5, snowflake = 4

PAGE 55

I'M SICK OF MILK AND
COOKIES AND SOOT MAKES
ME SNEEZE

PAGE 56-57

ROUND 1

1. James Webb
2. Limerick
3. Your ankle
4. White
5. One Direction
6. Squid
7. Blue, yellow, black, green and red
8. Benedict Cumberbatch
9. The Flanders
10. England

ROUND 2

1. Avocado
2. Eight
3. Leveret
4. Kerry
5. Blue
6. Ear
7. It makes objects levitate
8. Ukraine
9. Reykjavík
10. Denmark

ROUND 3

1. Mythical creatures
2. Green, white, red
3. A dog
4. Bamboo
5. Mullingar
6. Louth
7. Westlife
8. Murphy
9. Apples
10. Lightyear

ROUND 4

1. Qatar
2. World Wide Web
3. JRR Tolkien
4. Cavan, Donegal, Leitrim, Monaghan and Louth.
5. Charlie Bird
6. Gymnastics
7. WB Yeats
8. ÚII
9. Beyoncé
10. Radio Telifís Éireann

SHEILA ARMSTRONG is a writer and editor from Sligo. She has worked on many children's books, including *The Great Irish Weather Book*, *The Great Irish Science Book*, *The Friendship Fairies* series and *What Makes Us Human*. She writes *The Great Big Irish Annual* series with Gill Books every year. She loves puns, terrible jokes, and when dogs look like their owners.

Gill Books
Hume Avenue
Park West
Dublin 12
www.gillbooks.ie

Gill Books is an imprint of M.H. Gill and Co.

© Gill Books 2022

9780717195060

Text by Sheila Armstrong
Designed by grahamthew.com
Print origination by Sarah McCoy
Illustrations by Jacky Sheridan
Printed by Hussar Books, Poland

For permission to reproduce photographs, the author and publisher gratefully acknowledge the following:

© Adobe Stock: 43C; © Africa Studio/Shutterstock: 30TL; © Allan Cash Picture Library/Alamy: 50TL; © Bazonka/Wikimedia Commons: 2C; © Bettman/Getty Images: 2TR; © Bruno Passigatti/Shutterstock: 6BR; © Carl Berkeley/Wikimedia Commons: 2TL; Courtesy of Gillian Horgan: 14TR; Courtesy of Richie Stokes: 24TL; © Dani Simmonds/Shutterstock: 34TL; © D. Ribeiro/Shutterstock: 12C; © Eamonn O'Mahony/Wikimedia Commons: 11TR; © Fehmiu Roffytavare/Shutterstock: 36C; © Freepik: 1BL, 3C, 4BR, 5TL, 6BC, 7BR, 9UTR, 9LTR, 9CR, 13C, 14LC, 15TR, 15BL, 15TL, 15TL, 20TR, 28BR, 32BL, 33CR, 34BL, 36BL, 37CL, 39TL, 42TR, 46CR, 46CL, 47TR, 48BL, 51TL, 52C, 53BL; © Gary Carr/INPHO: 30C; © iStock/Getty Premium: 3BR, 3BL, 4TR, 5TR, 5BC, 6TR, 7TR, 8TR, 8BL, 8TL, 8TC, 9BC, 16C, 17C, 18C, 18TL, 20LC, 25TL, 28TR, 32BR, 33BL, 33TL, 36TL, 36TC, 37C, 37BR, 39TR, 39C, 42C, 42C, 42C, 42BL, 42BC, 42BR, 43BL, 44C, 45TR, 50C, 51C, 53C, 53TL, 55TR, 55TC; © Mario Hagen/Shutterstock: 50BL; © National Library of Norway/Wikimedia Commons: 39BR; © ShelleyAllenArt/Shutterstock: 35TR, 35TC; © Vladimir Borozenets/Shutterstock: 20BL; © Wikimedia Commons: 18TL, 38TR, 39RC; © Willowpix/Shutterstock: 31BR

The author and publisher have made every effort to trace all copyright holders, but if any have been inadvertently overlooked we would be pleased to make the necessary arrangement at the first opportunity.

This book is typeset in Neue Kabel and Tomarik.

The paper used in this book comes from the wood pulp of sustainably managed forests.

A CIP catalogue record for this book is available from the British Library.

54321